by Sue Atwater
illustrated by Louise Ellis

Harcourt
SCHOOL PUBLISHERS

Printed in China

ISBN 10: 0-15-350501-X
ISBN 13: 978-0-15-350501-0

Ordering Options
ISBN 10: 0-15-350333-5 (Grade 3 Below-Level Collection)
ISBN 13: 978-0-15-350333-7 (Grade 3 Below-Level Collection)
ISBN 10: 0-15-357489-5 (package of 5)
ISBN 13: 978-0-15-357489-4 (package of 5)

3 4 5 6 7 8 9 10 985 12 11 10 09 08

Lee's new school looked terrific. It was clean, bright, and colorful. No other children were there yet, because school hadn't started. Lee and her mother had come to meet her teacher.

"I can't wait for school to start!" said Lee. "It's exciting being in a new school!"

Second grade at her old school had been fun. She had become a better reader and she had learned to like writing, too. She often drew pictures to go along with the stories she wrote.

Mrs. Kyle smiled and beckoned to Lee and her mother. "Don't mind this clutter," she said. "I'll have it all cleaned up by Monday."

"I think it looks really nice," said Lee.

"Your mother mentioned that you like writing," said Mrs. Kyle. "You'll have many chances to write since we write every day."

"I'm ready!" said Lee.

Monday finally came and Lee was really excited when she got to her classroom. She looked around the room. All the other children seemed ready, too.

Mrs. Kyle pointed to the board and said, "Here's our daily schedule." Lee stared in shock. She couldn't read it.

Daily Schedule
Monday
Reading 10:00 am
Writing 11:00 am

The letters looked all curly because it was not printing. It was grown-up writing. She could make out only the words *Math* and *Lunch*. What would she do?

The whole day, Lee was flustered. Nothing Mrs. Kyle put on the board was printed. Everything appeared in flowing letters that Lee couldn't read.

The next day was even worse. All the other kids used grown-up writing! They wrote their names in it, and they did their work with it. Lee tried adding swirls to her letters, but they did not look right. She didn't know what to do.

Lee hoped it wasn't visible how upset she was. At recess, Mrs. Kyle asked, "Are you okay, Lee?"

Lee nodded and replied, "I think so, Mrs. Kyle." She was not so sure, though.

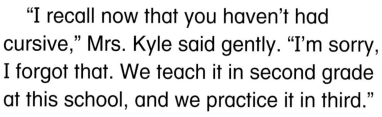

"I recall now that you haven't had cursive," Mrs. Kyle said gently. "I'm sorry, I forgot that. We teach it in second grade at this school, and we practice it in third."

"I guess I have a lot of practicing to do!" said Lee.

"Don't worry, Lee," Mrs. Kyle said. "You'll learn very soon. I know you like to draw. Think of cursive writing as artwork."

Mrs. Kyle's remark made Lee feel a little better. That night, Mrs. Kyle called Lee's mother at home. The next night, Mrs. Kyle came to Lee's house.

She brought Lee some worksheets that showed how to make each letter. Mrs. Kyle gave Lee a white board to use. At the top was the alphabet in cursive, and beneath it were lines for Lee to use. She could practice and erase again and again.

At first, it was hard for Lee to make the letters. She frowned at them, but she kept trying day after day. Slowly, she began to find cursive easier to read in class. She began to get faster at writing it, too.

In a few months, Lee's cursive was as good as anyone's. She did not write fast, but she wrote very neatly. At the Fall Festival, Mrs. Kyle gave her an award that said "Fearless."

"Why *fearless*?" asked Lee.

"You have overcome the cursive crisis!" said Mrs. Kyle with a big smile.

Think Critically

1. Why was Lee surprised on the first day of school?

2. How did Mrs. Kyle help solve Lee's problem of not knowing cursive?

3. How would you describe Lee?

4. Do you think the school year will get better or worse for Lee? Explain your answer.

5. Would you have acted the same way as Lee? Why or why not?

 Social Studies

Write a Report! Choose any social studies topic that interests you. For example, you might find some facts about the state or town where you live. Write a short report in your best handwriting!

School-Home Connection Lee got a surprise when she went to her new school. Some surprises are good; some are not so good. Ask family members to tell stories of the best surprises they ever had.

Word Count: 551